SPMG
HEINEMANN MATHEMATICS 1
Name
SHAPE WORKBOOK
AF073601
Revised

I

In space

Match

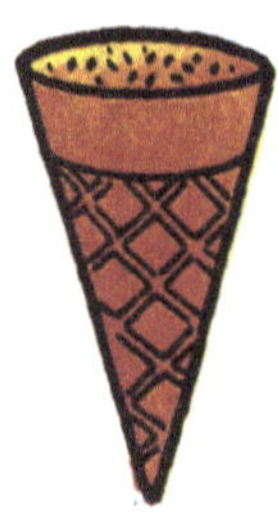

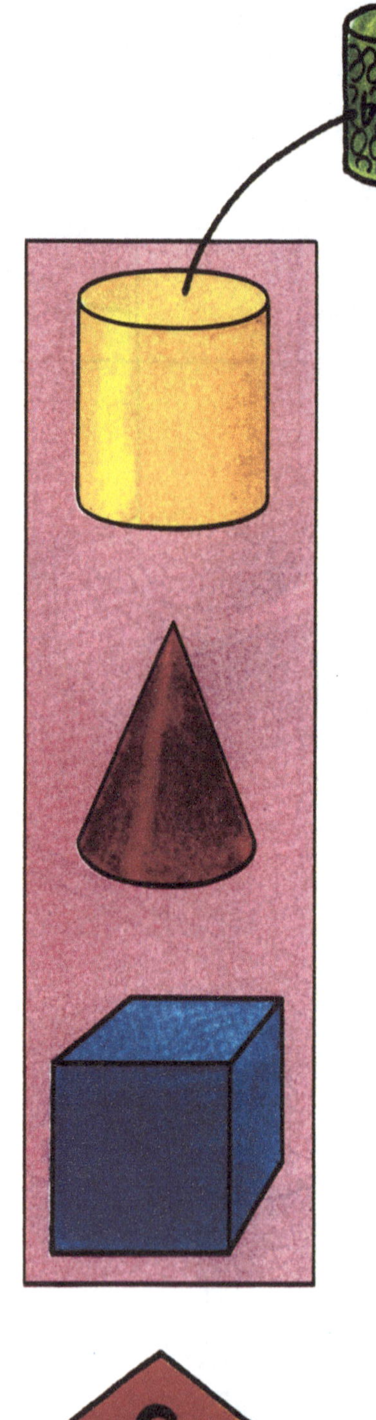

The Party

Colour **[cuboid shape]** How many? ☐

Colour **[cylinder shape]** How many? ☐

Colour **[sphere shape]** How many? ☐

In space

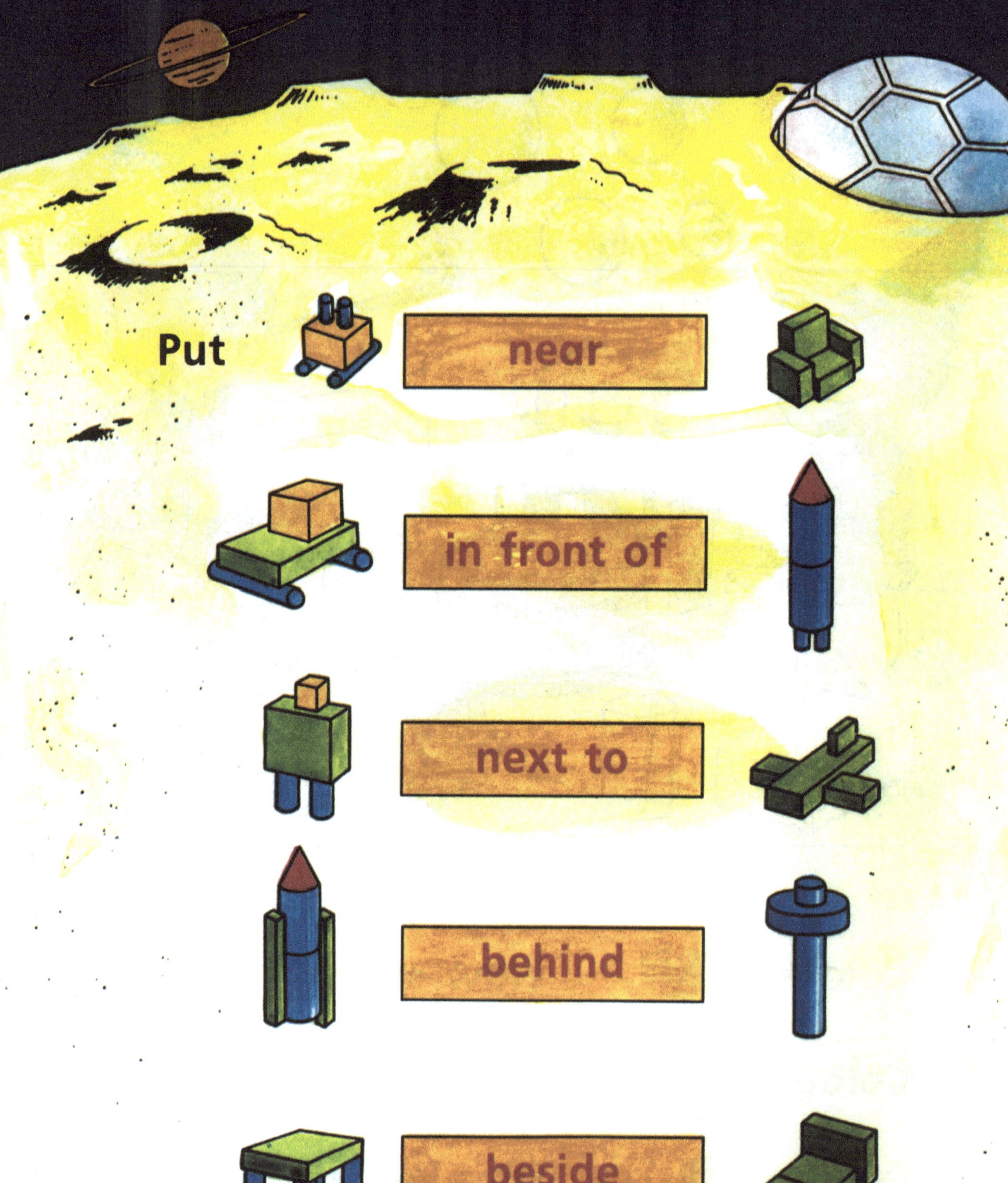

Positional language
6
Colour
the one above
the one at the bottom
the one inside
the one on top

A shape journey

Talk, make, tell a story.

Shape pictures

9

Match

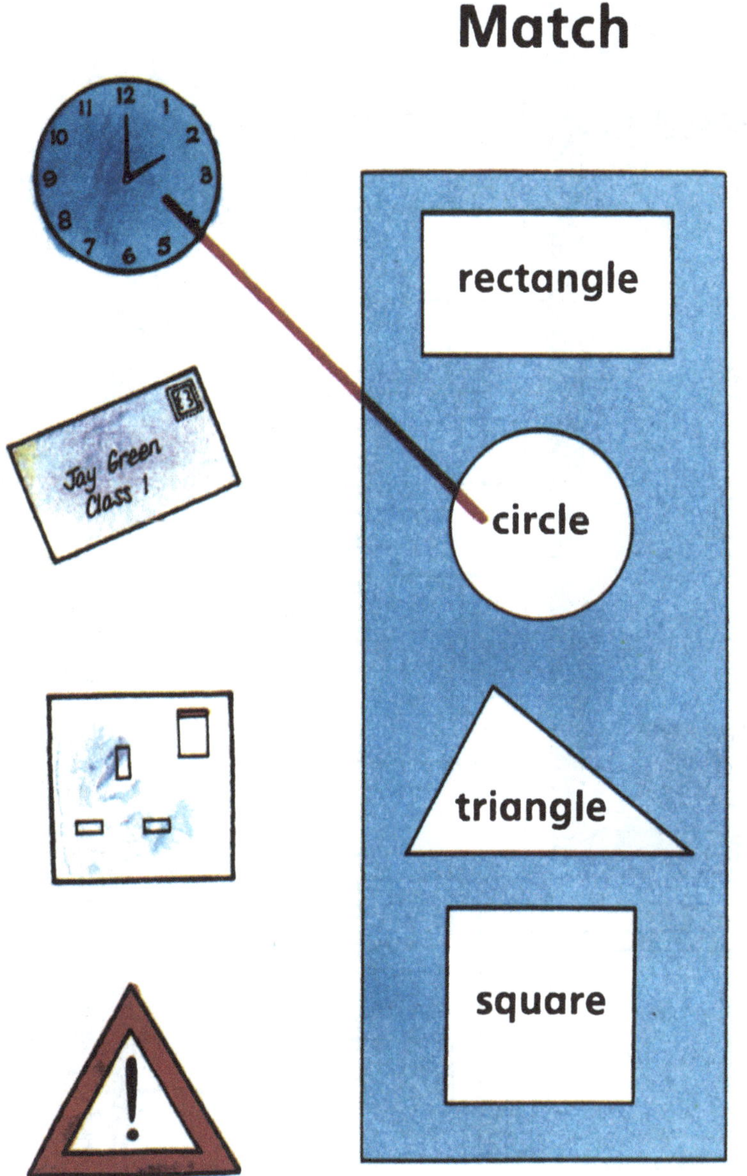

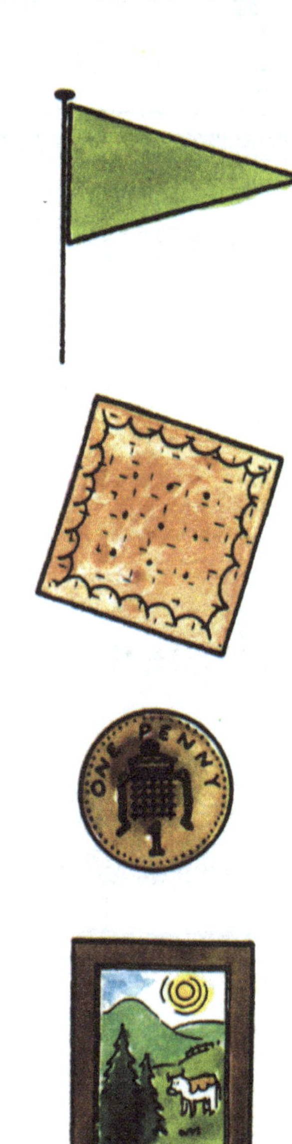

rectangle
circle
triangle
square
Jay Green
Class 1

ONE PENNY

a sail
a square
window
a round
window

Draw

The Station
Colour the
squares
triangles
circles
rectangles
PRIVATE
LEFT LUGGAGE
LEFT LUGGAGE
LITTER
RED STAR

DAILY NEWS

How many

squares

triangles

circles

rectangles?

Find the paths.

Colour triangles ▲.   Colour circles ●.

Finish each pattern.

Cut and stick.

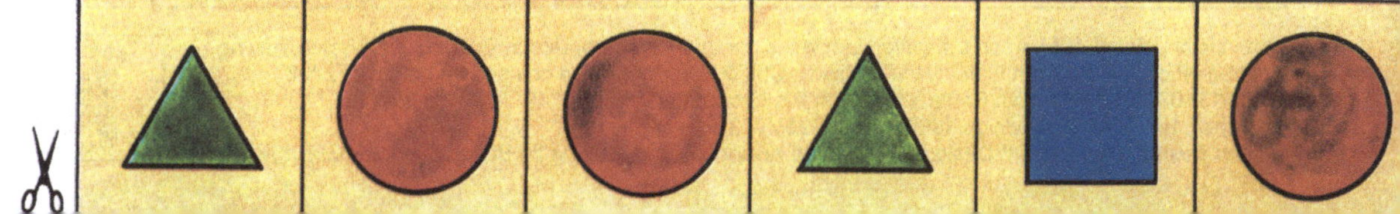

Ties

Finish each pattern.

Make patterns.

1	2	3	4	5	6	7	8	9	10	11	12	13	14	15

Heinemann is an imprint of Pearson Education Limited, a company incorporated in England and Wales, having its registered office at Edinburgh Gate, Harlow, Essex, CM20 2JE.Registered company number: 872828
ISBN 978 0 435 03090 2 © Scottish Primary Mathematics Group 1991.
First published 1991. Revised edition 1995.   25   30
Typeset and illustrated by Oxprint Design. Printed and bound in Great Britain by Bell & Bain Ltd, Glasgow